2 9 NOV 2019

bSF
RF

Please return on or before the latest date above.
You can renew online at www.kent.gov.uk/libs
or by phone 08458 247 200

CUSTOMER SERVICE EXCELLENCE

Libraries & Archives

Kent
County
Council

Badger Publishing Limited
Suite G08, Business & Technology Centre
Bessemer Drive, Stevenage, Hertfordshire SG1 2DX
Telephone: 01438 791037   Fax: 01438 791036
www.badger-publishing.co.uk

The Incredible Save ISBN 978-1-84926-259-0

Badger Publishing would like to thank Jonny Zucker
for his help in putting this series together.

Publisher: David Jamieson
Editor: Danny Pearson
Design: Fiona Grant
Illustration: Paul Savage
Printed and bound in China through Colorcraft Ltd., Hong Kong

THE INCREDIBLE SAVE

CONTENTS

Badger Publishing

New words:

half	shoulder
started	incredibly
incredible	silent
stared	believe

Main characters:

Luke

Josh

Matt

Don

CHAPTER 1

On The Bench

Matt was fed up.

He'd joined Thornton United a few weeks ago but he still hadn't played a match.

This was the third game in a row that Don, the manager, had put him on the subs bench.

The problem was that Matt was a striker and Thornton already had two good strikers-Josh and Luke.

Today the team was playing away at Delton. Delton were top of the league.

But incredibly, Thornton were 2-0 up at half time.

Both Josh and Luke had scored and the Thornton team had begun to believe they could win.

But just as the second half began, things started to go wrong.

Delton took a corner.

The ball flew high in the air.
Luke and Zach, the Thornton goalie,
ran and jumped for the ball at the same
time.

The ball came off Zach's shoulder and
went out of play.

But Luke and Zach smashed into one
another and crashed to the ground.

Don ran onto the pitch.

Matt got to his feet.

"If Luke has to come off," he thought,
"then this is my chance!"

Don checked on the fallen players.
Luke got up right away but Zach was in
pain.

Matt sat back down, as Don helped
Zach off the pitch.
"Look's like you're on!" Don shouted to
Matt.

Matt stared at the manager, in horror.
"But I'm not a goalie!" he said.

"I know," said Don. "but we don't have
another goalie. So just do your best,
mate."

Matt pulled on the goalie's gloves and
went to stand between the goal posts.
"I should be feeling great," he thought,
"but I just feel sick."

This wasn't what his first game for
Thornton was meant to be like!

CHAPTER 2

Goals Galore

It was another corner for Delton.

One of their players kicked the ball hard.

It flew high in the air and another player headed it straight at Matt's face.

Matt closed his eyes and put his hands in front of his face.

Incredibly, the ball smacked into Matt's hands and was saved.

Don leapt off the bench.

"Great save, Matt!" he yelled.

But the ball rolled away and landed right at the feet of a Delton player.

Before Matt knew what was happening, the player had tapped the ball into the back of the net.

Matt's team mates couldn't believe it!

He had somehow managed to save a goal and let one in- all in ten seconds!

As the game went on, Matt wished a hole would swallow him up.

Every few minutes, a ball seemed to shoot past him and hit the back of the net.

Delton were 5-2 up and looked like winning after all.

Josh was very angry they were losing and the very next time Delton looked like scoring, he ran into the box and tripped up the Delton player who had the ball.

Matt couldn't believe it!

The ref blew his whistle and gave Delton a penalty.

"Thanks a bunch, mate!" Matt said to Josh.

Josh got a red card and a ticking off from Don. A Delton player put the ball on the spot.

The whistle went and he kicked the ball hard.

Matt took a chance and dived to his left.
The ball hit him smack in the chest, just
as the ref blew the final whistle.

Don leapt off the bench.
"Incredible save! Well done, Matt!"
he shouted.

But all around him, Matt's team mates
were silent.

Exhausted, Matt walked off the pitch.

CHAPTER 3

Ignored

"Well done Matt," said Luke,
as they got on the minibus to go home.
"Thanks to you we lost!"

"Yeah, thanks a bunch, mate!" said
Josh. "We were 2-0 up before you came
on!"

"Give Matt a break, will you?" Don
shouted, "Football's a team game.
We all lost that game-not just Matt!"

No one said anything to Matt after that.
But no one would sit next to him either.

So Matt sat up the front, on his own, behind the driver's seat.

Matt did up his seat belt and stared out of the window, as Don started the engine and pulled out of the car park.

The traffic in town was slow and it seemed to take ages to reach the motorway.

But once they were on it, the bus started to pick up speed.

Don flicked the indicator on and moved out into the fast lane.

Up ahead, Matt saw a sign.

The turn off for Thornton was just
fifteen miles away.

"Another half an hour," he thought
"and I'll be home." Which was exactly
where Matt wanted to be, right then.

"Matt! Matt!"
Don suddenly said
"I don't feel too ..."

Matt looked up and saw Don slump
forward onto the steering wheel.
A car blasted its horn as the minibus
drifted into the outside lane.

Everyone froze!

CHAPTER 4
Out of Control!

For half a second, no one moved. Then Matt undid his seat belt and leapt to his feet.

Leaning over Don, he grabbed the wheel, and yanked the bus back into the middle lane.

"Luke!" he yelled, "Get someone to phone an ambulance and then come and help."

Luke looked terrified but did as he was told.

"We're going too fast." said Matt,
"Get Don's foot off the accelerator, will
you, while I steer."

Luke bent down and grabbed at Don's
right foot. "I can't shift it!" he said,
"His foot's jammed!"

Matt tried not to panic.

"Okay," he said, "switch on the hazard
lights and keep your hand on the horn.
I'm going to drive onto the hard
shoulder."

"No! Don't! Not yet!" yelled Luke,
looking in the wing mirror.

Up ahead, Matt could see red brake lights coming on.

"We've got to go now!" he shouted, "Or we'll crash into the cars in front!"

Luke spotted a small gap in the traffic.

"Okay. NOW!" he yelled.

Matt held the wheel tightly and steered into the inside lane.

There was a screech of brakes and a sharp blast on a horn, as he crossed in front of a van and drove onto the hard shoulder.

"You did it! You did it!" Luke grinned,
patting Matt on the shoulder.

But Matt wasn't grinning.

He had just seen something up ahead.

CHAPTER 5
Trouble Ahead

"Look!" Matt yelled "There's a car!"

Ahead of them, blocking the hard shoulder, at the bottom of the hill, was a broken down car.

"STOP! You've got to stop!" yelled Luke. "There are people in that car!"

Matt took one hand off the steering wheel and switched off the engine.

The bus slowed but it did not stop.

It started rolling down the hill, towards the car, picking up speed again, as it went.

"We're going to hit the car!" yelled Luke.

Matt could see the driver rushing to get his family out of the car.

"Get back in your seat and hold on tight!" Matt yelled at Luke. "I'm going to steer into the fence."

There was no time for Luke to do up his seat belt.
As the bus crashed against the fence, he was thrown forward.
He let out a yell as his nose smashed into the seat in front.

Again and again, Matt steered into the fence and the bus slowed a little.

"We're going to hit the car!" everyone yelled.

Matt closed his eyes and steered the bus into the fence, one last time.

There was a loud scraping noise and the sound of breaking glass, as the bus finally came to a stop.

Matt opened his eyes.

He had missed the car by a metre!

Exhausted, Matt fell back into his seat.

All around him, his team mates were silent.

CHAPTER 6

Just Rewards

Matt looked round. Luke was holding his nose.

He was in pain and his hands were sticky with blood but he managed to grin at Matt.

Incredibly, everyone else was okay.

Josh undid his seat belt and stood up.

He began to clap and before long everyone was on their feet, clapping and cheering and grinning at Matt.

Then Don started to come round, and the car driver helped him and the boys get out of the bus, just as an ambulance pulled up.

Don spent the night in hospital
but was soon back on his feet.

And as for Luke, his nose was broken,
so he couldn't play football for while.

So, at long last, Matt got the chance to
show his team mates that he was a
better goal scorer than a goal saver!

And when Don handed out Thornton
United's football awards at the end of
the season, there was a special award
for Matt.

"This is from us all," Don said to Matt,
"to say thank you for saving our lives."

Matt grinned and lifted the silver
trophy in the air.

Everyone clapped and cheered.

Matt looked at the trophy. It said...

MATT SHEPHERD
~WINNER ~
SAVE OF THE YEAR AWARD

GOALS

An Incredible Goalkeeper

In 2000, Lev Yashin was voted the best goalkeeper of the 20th century. This Russian footballer saved an incredible 150 penalties.

The Fastest Goal

In 1998, in Argentina, Ricarde Olivera scored a goal for his club, it was scored just 2.8 seconds into a match!

Fastest Own Goal

The Torquay player, Pat Kruse holds the record for the fastest own goal- just 8 seconds into a match, in 1977.

The Most Goals
The most goals scored in an international match was 31, when Australia beat American Samoa 31-0, in 2001.

Unusual Goal Scorers
It isn't just footballers that score goals.

"Balloon gets goal for Sunderland"
When: Sunderland v Liverpool - Oct 2009.

How: The football hit a balloon on the pitch and popped into the goal!

"Dog heads in goal"
When: Knave of Clubs v Newcastle Town - Nov 1985.

How: A dog ran on to the pitch and headed the ball into the net.

QUESTIONS

- *Why was it hard for Matt to get a game at Thornton United?*

- *Why did Matt not want to go on when Zach came off?*

- *Matt saved one goal and a penalty. Was this luck or skill?*

- *While Matt steered the minibus, what did Luke do to help?*

- *What two things did Matt do to slow the bus down on the hard shoulder?*

- *How did Luke break his nose?*

- *How did Matt get his chance to play as a striker?*

- *What special award did Matt get from his football club?*